5—

Beautiful Roses

Beautiful Roses

Text by P. Svoboda

Illustrations by J. Kaplická

SPRING BOOKS

Translated by Kevin Hartshorne
Graphic design by V. Ungermann

Designed and produced by
ARTIA for SPRING BOOKS
DRURY HOUSE • RUSSELL STREET • LONDON WC2

First edition 1965
Second impression 1966

© Copyright 1965 Artia
Printed in Czechoslovakia by Svoboda, Prague
S 1937

CONTENTS

The Evolution of the Garden Rose

In ancient times roses were grown in large numbers in Persia. *R. gallica* is reputed to have been a religious emblem of the Medes and Persians in the 12th century B.C. The cultivated rose reached Greece, and later Rome, through Armenia, Thrace and Macedonia. At the time of the fall of the Roman Empire roses were grown on a considerable scale in Rome and Egypt, and the cut blooms were used lavishly on all festive occasions. After Rome fell the cultivation of roses was continued in Asia, and the Arabs, who penetrated North Africa to Spain, gave them an honoured place in their courtyard gardens.

In Greece the rose was the symbol of Aphrodite — the goddess of fertility, love and beauty — in Rome the symbol of Venus, and Christianity afterwards dedicated the flower to the Virgin Mary. In Southern Europe the cultivation of roses developed in Italy, gaining great popularity during the period of the Wars of the Crusades. At this time the rose was also grown widely in France.

At the beginning of the 19th century the development of garden roses acquired a new impetus, mainly due to the establishment of an extensive collection made at Malmaison by the Empress Josephine. By 1814 this probably comprised all rose species and varieties then known. At that time the creation of new varieties of roses was mainly a haphazard affair: crosses arose on the whole spontaneously in such collections, since artificial cross-pollination, using carefully selected male and female parents, was apparently not practised. In the suitable climatic conditions of Western Europe, the seeds of types of roses ripened that would not have done so farther to the east. Sowing and gathering the blooms was often carried out on a large scale with success, and throughout the 19th century novelties in roses were largely a monopoly of England and France.

We can divide roses into two broad groups: *wild roses* or *species*, and *garden* or *cultivated roses* which have been developed by the hybridist. The species constitute the basic material from which man has created a great number of cultivated forms. There is much disagreement among botanists regarding the classification of different species. However, fewer than 200 are usually regarded as sufficiently distinct to warrant separate recognition. Present-day roses are descended from about one dozen species or ancient cultivated forms thereof.

Practically all classification carried out up to the present time has been unsatisfactory. Repeated crossing of the original forms disguises them so much that it is often impossible to judge their origin and group them on this basis. Even today the parentage of many novelties is not recorded by the hybridist. Therefore the classification and grouping of the various kinds of roses is on the whole artificial, and usually done according to the individual characteristics of the rose.

The more important of the different groups of roses and of the 'foundation' species or wild roses are described in the following pages.

R. gallica L.

This species occurs throughout Southern and Central Europe, in the Middle East and the Caucasus. It played an important role in the rise of the old European cultivated roses. In various places and during various periods numerous varieties sprang from *R. gallica*: the full-flowered type was cultivated near Provins, where it was used in many forms for the making of conserves. In the second half of the 19th century more than 600 varieties were known.

Double forms of *R. gallica* have been grown since ancient times and it has been termed the foundation species from which most of our garden roses were evolved. It was, in fact, the common ancestor of the gallicas, damasks, Provence and moss varieties and the alba roses. *R. rubiginosa* (*eglanteria*), *R. wichuraiana*, *R. chinensis* and *R. rugosa* — forms or varieties of all these species have at various times contributed to the development of the rose as we know it today.

R. damascena Miller

This rose is usually regarded as a cross between *R. gallica* and *R. phoenicia*. It was brought from the Orient to Italy during the Middle Ages, and to France during the Wars of the Crusades, then also to Spain and England. The Autumn Damask rose (*R. bifera*) is thought to be *R. gallica* × *R. moschata*. All the damask roses are strongly scented.

R. centifolia L.

The cabbage or Provence rose is not, as was once thought, a species, nor is it a simple primary hybrid. It is undoubtedly a hybrid between descendants of *R. canina, damascena, gallica* and *moschata*. According to Hurst (1941), *R. centifolia* was slowly evolved from the end of the 16th century to the end to the 19th century as the result of the skill of Dutch hybridists. The nodding, deep-centred, globular blooms are very full and richly scented.

R. centifolia muscosa Seringe

The earliest date mentioned for the existence of the Common Moss is 1696 when it was cultivated at Carcassonne. It was grown in Holland in 1720 and in England in 1735, and is characterised by thick, glandular and moss-like growths on the calyx. France and England were responsible for the creation of numerous moss roses, including Shailer's White Moss (1788), Comtesse de Murinais (1843), Blanche Moreau (1880) and Gloire des Mousseux (1852).

R. alba L.

Almost certainly a natural hybrid which probably originated in South Asia. It may well have been a hybrid between *R. damascena* and *R. canina*. *R. alba semiplena* is thought to be the original *R. alba* and is probably the traditional Jacobite rose. All forms and varieties of *R. alba* are upright growers, with few prickles and distinct, grey-green foliage. Céleste and Maiden's Blush are typical examples.

Tea Roses

The name tea rose refers to supposed hybrids between *R. chinensis* and *R. gigantea*. *R. chinensis* was not discovered until towards the end of the 18th century when *R. gigantea* was also introduced. Hurst describes four such basic hybrids which had a far-reaching influence on the development of the modern garden rose — Slater's Crimson China (1792), Parson's Pink China (1793), Hume's Blush Tea-scented China (1809) and Park's Yellow Tea-scented China (1824).

The variety Devoniensis (Forester, 1838), a most attractive creamy-white and blush, was an important parent. By the eighteen-eighties there were about 600 varieties, all with restrained colouring and elegant form. Today they have almost disappeared because of their low resistance to frosts. Popular varieties of teas were: Safrano (Beauregard, 1839) and Papa Gontier (Nabonnand, 1883), which were for a long period exported from the Riviera in winter, together with Mlle Marie van Houtte (Ducher, 1871), Maman Cochet (Cochet, 1892), Catherine Mermet (Guillot, 1869) and others. Some were climbers: Belle Lyonnaise (Levet, 1869) and Gloire de Dijon (Jacotot, 1853). In the Nikitinsky Botanical Gardens in Yalta in the Crimea, the following teas are cultivated: Marusya, Pobeditel, Rodina, Fantaziya, Zhelannaya (N. D. Kostetskiy, 1931-45).

R. noisettiana Thory

The first Noisette, introduced in 1811, was Champney's Pink Cluster (Miller's White Musk × Parson's Pink China). In 1828 Aimée Vibert (Vibert, 1828) was introduced and it formed the foundation of a number of other varieties, some of climbing habit. At the end of the 19th century there were 300, the most famous including Chromatella (Coquereau, 1843), William Allen Richardson (Veuve Ducher, 1878) and Mme Alfred Carrière (1879). But in the course of time the Noisettes disappeared because of crossing with other groups, above all with the teas.

R. borboniana Desp.

The first Bourbon was a natural hybrid between *R. chinensis* and *R. damascena semperflorens*. It originated on the French island of Bourbon (Réunion) in 1817. The seed was taken to the garden of the French grower M. Jacqueson in Neuilly in 1819, and formed the basis for the *R. borboniana* group, at one time widely known and valued for their repeat blooming. At the close of the 19th century about 500 varieties were known. Still in cultivation are the varieties: Souvenir de la Malmaison (Béluze, 1843), Hermosa (Marcheseau, 1840), Zéphirine Drouhin (1858) and Adam Messerich (P. Lambert, 1920). Hurst observes: 'Crossed with Hume's Blush China it (the Bourbon rose) helped to create our pink tea roses, and it was the main source of the typical hybrid perpetuals . . .'

Hybrid Perpetuals

This group was aptly defined by Shepherd in 1954 as 'a combination of almost all the major groups of garden roses that preceded it'. Hybrid chinas, bourbons, noisettes and damasks were probably the chief parents.

The hybrid perpetuals were at the peak of their popularity from 1840 to 1890. The colour range embraced white, pink and red in various hues and tones, but no yellow varieties were produced. In 1884 the catalogue of William Paul & Sons of Cheshunt in Hertfordshire listed over 800 hybrid perpetuals.

Unlike the teas, the hybrid perpetuals were resistant to low temperatures. Consequently no winter protection was needed and they flourished even with 'rough' treatment on the part of the gardener. Some varieties were decidedly prone to mildew, but the majority produced some autumn flowers.

Among the best-known varieties, some of which are still available, are: Mrs John Laing (Bennett, 1887), Général Jacqueminot (Roussel, 1853), Ulrich Brunner Fils (A. Levet, 1881), Paul Neyron (A. Levet, 1869), Georg Arends (B. Finner, 1910), Baronne Prévost (Desprez, 1842), Fisher-Holmes (E. Verdier, 1865), Victor Verdier (Lacharme, 1851), and Alfred Colomb (Lacharme, 1865). The first white variety was Frau Karl Druschki (P. Lambert, 1901) which was perfectly formed but without scent.

The Pernet Roses

These were named in honour of the hybridist J. Pernet-Ducher of Lyon. They are crosses between *R. foetida persiana* (Persian Yellow) and the hybrid perpetuals. The first variety was Soleil d'Or (J. Pernet-Ducher, 1900), which arose from crossing *R. foetida persiana* with the hybrid perpetual Antoine Ducher (Ducher, 1866), and became the foundation of a large series of beautifully coloured roses, mostly in various shades of yellow and orange. With this combination the large-bloomed roses gained a new golden-yellow colour, which brought out all the other nuances of the old hybrids. A shortcoming of the pernet roses was a low resistance to mildew and black spot, and early dropping of the leaves. The most important varieties in this class were: Souvenir de Claudius Pernet (Pernet-Ducher, 1920), Mevrouw G. A. van Rossem (van Rossem, 1926), Julien Potin or Golden Pernet (Pernet-Ducher, 1927), Heinrich Wendland (Kordes, 1930), Hinrich Gaede (Kordes, 1931) and Angels Mateu (P. Dot, 1932).

Today the pernet roses are no longer regarded as a separate group and are in fact merged with the hybrid teas.

Hybrid Teas

The hybrid perpetuals crossed with the teas led to the hybrid teas which were the mainstay of the contemporary rose garden until the floribundas started to threaten their popularity shortly after World War II. Hybrid teas can be readily cut and forced; they bloom freely and continuously and have an exceptionally wide range of colours; many are strongly scented, and in most cases they are reasonably tolerant of lower winter temperatures.

Some of the older varieties are still cultivated: La France (1867), Ophelia (1912) and Etoile de Hollande (1919).

Large-bloomed Climbers

Amongst large-bloomed roses there are some varieties with the tendency to climb. The tea rose Maréchal Niel throws out shoots up to 12 ft long, and some climbing sports of hybrid teas are just as adept at climbing. These climbing hybrid teas need careful attention if they are to bloom freely. The main shoots should be trained horizontally or fan-wise, and not upwards. This treatment encourages the production of laterals and sub-laterals which carry the majority of blooms. Hard pruning must be avoided, since this may lead to reversion to the bush form. Climbing Ena Harkness, Climbing Etoile de Hollande and Climbing Mrs Sam McGredy are typical.

R. chinensis minima (Sims) Voss

At the end of the 19th century only 17 varieties of this flower-pot rose were known. Today it is returning to fashion, and a number of varieties have been raised in Spain, Holland and Germany. The best-known are: Bo-Peep, Midget, Pixie, Red Elf, Red Imp, Tom Thumb, Sweet Fairy (J. de Vink), Baby Gold Star or Estrellita de Oro, Perla de Alcanada, Perla de Montserrat, Para-Ti or Pour Toi, Coralin, Perla Rosa, Rosina (P. Dot), Zwergkönig and Zwergkönigin (W. Kordes), Baby Masquerade (M. Tantau, 1955). All are continuous-flowering, and the majority bear tiny, perfectly formed blooms with proportionately diminutive foliage, on plants up to 12 in. high.

R. wichuraiana Crépin

This semi-evergreen rose probably originated in the territory near the Yellow Sea, and is therefore not markedly resistant to severe frost when trained upright. If allowed to trail on the soil (when it makes a most effective ground cover) it is definitely hardier. It was brought from Japan to Europe by Wichura in 1887. Through crossing with tea roses and hybrid perpetuals numerous large-bloomed varieties were created. American Pillar (van Fleet, 1902), Dorothy Perkins

14

(Jackson and Perkins, 1901), Dr W. van Fleet (van Fleet, 1910), Excelsa (Walsh, 1909) and Silver Moon (van Fleet, 1910) are typical. The wichuraianas are classed as ramblers, and are suitable for pillars, arches and pergolas, but not walls where they succumb to mildew. They bloom once only and are usually resistant to black spot.

Polyantha Pompons

These are mostly dwarf hybrids of R. multiflora and are discussed on p. 18.

Hybrid Musks

The so-called hybrid musks began in 1904 when Peter Lambert, the German hybridist, raised the rosy-white Trier, one of whose ancestors was R. moschata. The varieties subsequently evolved by the Rev. J. H. Pemberton had little to do with this species. Most of Pemberton's seedlings were crosses between Trier and hybrid teas. They are still popular in the British Isles, although not sufficiently hardy to stand Central European frosts. All are markedly fragrant, bloom more or less continuously from June to autumn, and are best left unpruned when they will make excellent shrubs. Some, notably Felicia, Moonlight and Prosperity, make fine 5 to 6 ft hedges.

R. kordesii

This group of roses combines the hardiness of R. rugosa with the large blooms of the garden roses and the continuous blooming of the climbing roses. Originated by Wilhelm Kordes, R. kordesii was derived from an open-pollinated seed of Max Graf (R. rugosa × R. wichuraiana). Some varieties are best treated as potential flowering shrubs, others as climbers. The pale yellow Leverkusen (1955) and the dark rose-pink Ritter von Barmstede (1960) are typical varieties.

Floribundas

These roses are discussed on p. 18.

Shrub Roses

Shrub roses include those of quite diverse origins, for amongst them are various species and their relatively simple crosses. They are hardy and thus in no need of protection, but suitable for use in parks and open country. The group can be subdivided according to the original types from which the individual varieties sprang. The bourbons, albas, gallicas, centifolias and damasks are treated as shrub roses, as opposed to the modern hybrid teas and floribundas which are grown primarily for bedding.

R. rugosa. Japanese or Ramanas Rose

This species comes from Northern China, Korea, Japan and the most eastern parts of the U.S.S.R. It was first brought to London in 1796. *R. rugosa* attracted hybridists because of its resistance to the cold, and there have been many successful attempts to enrich it with the qualities of the large-flowered roses. In parks the most often cultivated are the varieties Blanc Double de Coubert (Cochet-Cochet, 1892), Conrad Ferdinand Meyer (Müller, 1899), F. J. Grootendorst (de Goey, 1918), Hildebrandseck (P. Lambert, 1909), Schneezwerg (P. Lambert, 1912), Mme George Bruant (Bruant, 1888), Ruskin (van Fleet, 1928), Sanguinaire (Guillot, 1933), Stern von Prag (V. Berger, 1926), Dr Eckener (V. Berger, 1930). *R. rugosa* has been used in Russia by I. V. Michurin and in Canada by F. L. Skinner, among other hybridists.

The rugosas do especially well on light, sandy soil, but they will succeed almost anywhere except where the soil is chalky or drainage is very poor. All varieties are very fragrant, and make spreading shrubs with many small prickles and deeply veined, rich green foliage. They flower more or less continuously from the end of May well into autumn. The heps are usually conspicuous.

R. rugosa hollandica is widely used as a stem for budding standard roses. Standards budded on this stock are highly resistant to drought, but are very prone to 'suckering', hence the need for firm support at all times.

R. spinosissima L. Burnet or Scots Briar

This species is found from Europe to Central Asia. It has been crossed with numerous garden roses, and several types of beautiful and hardy shrub roses evolved. Crossings with hybrid teas by Kordes have produced Frühlingsgold (1937), Frühlingsmorgen (1942), Frühlingsduft (1949), Frühlingstag (1949) and Frühlingszauber (1942), among other varieties. All are of exceptional beauty and are strongly scented.

R. canina L.

This species is prized for its hardiness. It is of little value for garden display but is extensively used as a stock for budding bush roses and standards, especially in Britain. Over 100 variants are known, many carefully selected strains, originally developed by a particular nurseryman. Typical examples are Thornless Brög (R. Brög, 1902), *R. canina inermis* (Gamon, Lyon, 1905), Kokulinsky's Wild Rose (Kokulinsky, Berlin, 1900), Pfanders Canina (J. Pfander, Beuren, 1930), Pollmers Canina or Pavs rote Canina (Pollmer, Grosshain, 1904) and Schmids Ideal (R. Schmid, Kostritz).

R. rubiginosa or *R. eglanteria*. Sweet Briar or Eglantine

This species bears very fragrant, clear pink blooms in midsummer. The small, oval, red heps are equally pleasing. The foliage is also well scented, especially after a shower of rain.

The Penzance hybrid sweet briars raised by Lord Penzance in the eighteen-nineties were crosses with hybrid perpetuals, bourbons and *R. foetida*. They include Amy Robsart (1894), Lord Penzance (1894) and Julie Mannering (1895) and the majority grow to at least 7 ft with an equal spread. Unfortunately they are mostly rather prone to black spot.

R. foetida and *R. foetida bicolor*

See page 28 and accompanying illustration.

•

A classification of roses has been made by the National Rose Society of England and the following summary is based on the 1964 edition of the Society's publication *Roses — A Selected List of Varieties*. This attempts to group modern roses for garden purposes according to their appearance rather than their parentage. It divides the different varieties as follows:

The hybrid tea type. This includes all hybrid tea, hybrid perpetual, pernetiana, tea and large-flowered roses which are similar in form to those usually recognised as hybrid teas.

Examples: Ophelia (Paul, 1912), Mrs Sam McGredy (McGredy, 1939), Grand'mère Jenny (Meilland, 1950), My Choice (Le Grice, 1958), King's Ransom (Morey, 1961) and Blue Moon (Tantau, 1964).

Floribundas. This group includes varieties previously called hybrid polyanthas.

Examples: Else Poulsen (Poulsen, 1924) and Dainty Maid (Le Grice, 1938). All floribundas bear their blooms in medium to large clusters, in which many flowers open at the same time. Typical contemporary varieties include Paprika (Tantau, 1958), Masquerade (Boerner, 1950), Orange Sensation (de Ruiter, 1960), Scarlet Queen Elizabeth (Dickson, 1963) and Finale (Kordes, 1964).

An increasing number of recent floribundas are on the borderline between this group and the hybrid tea. These are described as floribunda-hybrid tea type. If disbudded to one bloom on a stem they will produce medium-sized, decorative, hybrid tea type flowers.

Examples: Faust (Kordes, 1960), Red Dandy (Norman, 1960), Sombrero (McGredy, 1962).

The floribunda dwarfs are small, low-growing plants to about 15 in. and are excellent for edgings. Doc (de Ruiter, 1956) is typical.

The polyantha pompons (sometimes known as polyanthas) are dwarf-growing cluster roses of similar habit to that of the floribundas, but with small individual blooms. Coral Cluster (Murrell, 1920) and Little Dorrit (Reeves, 1930) are examples, but the polyanthas are very little grown nowadays, most gardeners preferring the floribundas which have a much wider colour range.

The ramblers are mostly hybrids of *R. wichuraiana* or *R. multiflora*. American Pillar (van Fleet, 1902), Dorothy Perkins (Jackson and Perkins, 1901), Crimson Shower (Norman, 1951) and Dukat (Tantau, 1955) are typical.

Climbers are of stiffer growth and with larger individual blooms. Paul's Scarlet Climber (Paul, 1915), Mermaid (Paul, 1917) and Elegance (Brownell, 1937) are typical.

The miniature China roses are very dwarf, continuous-flowering bushes up to 12 in. in height. Their blooms are tiny and usually perfectly formed. Cinderella (de Vink, 1952) and Twinkles (Spek, 1954) are typical.

Shrub roses include both old and new varieties of similar flowering habit to the floribundas, but which usually grow too tall for formal beds. Some have a prefix to indicate the group which they most closely resemble; for example, Souvenir de la Malmaison which is usually termed a bourbon shrub.

Scent and Colour

The garden rose is valued not only for its form and the colour of its blooms, but also its scent, and the combination of these features has made it the most widely grown flower in the world.

The colour of the flowers differs according to the individual variety. In the living cells of the leaves there takes place a synthesis of colours during the process of crossing. Light and soil as well as genetic factors have a great influence on the forming of the colour substances. Therefore even the same variety is not necessarily exactly the same colour in different regions — this is particularly noticeable with bi-colours and multi-colours. The colouring of roses also varies in different years, and is dependent on the weather, for on the weather depends the amount of plant nutrients taken up by the bushes. A sudden drop in temperature can have a marked effect on the colour, and great heat in summer often causes pale colouring.

Scent also has a different strength in different places; for example, the blooms in Central Europe have a stronger scent than in southern countries. Scent in roses, as in other flowers, comes from the oils manufactured by the plant. These oils must volatilise before any perfume can be detected, and volatilisation depends on light, warmth and moisture. In cold, wet weather, scent is less pronounced, indeed it may be scarcely perceptible. A warm, humid day usually means that many roses will be strongly scented. There are, of course, substantial qualitative differences. Some varieties have scents like violets, others like lily-of-the-valley, apricots, apple blossom, verbena and honey.

The hybridist cannot produce a scented variety at will. Scent is a recessive rather than a dominant characteristic, hence the crossing of two very fragrant hybrid teas like Prima Ballerina and Sutter's Gold may well produce a seedling that is scentless.

Rose Hybridisation

Rose hybridisation is very old, and began at the time when little was known about heredity, and still less about genetics. The first breeders were mainly guided by instinct, and so the breeder 'works in an enchanting garden, tries to develop new roses, knowing what he wants and what he aims at, but not what he will achieve. The seed ripens under his care and is sown, but the result remains uncertain — only when the rose flowers will he know whether his hopes have been fulfilled or not' (R. Geschwind, 1866).

Although the importance and technique of planned crossing was not known, the discriminating choice of seedlings and sowing of the seed produced numerous worth-while varieties, especially in the warmer regions, where the seed ripens readily.

Contemporary hybridists are familiar with the theory of heredity but even extensive cytogenetic studies of roses (by C. C. Hurst in 1929, E. W. Erlanson from 1929 to 1934, and H. Rathlef in 1937, among others) did relatively little to assist the average breeder of new roses. In 1965 crossing is still sometimes carried out by trial and error. So often the old techniques are used, and occasionally beautiful roses are created, through the use of the ideas and work of the great hybridists of the past. It is certain that progress can only be gained by *planned* hybridisation.

Many varieties of roses developed also as natural variations or sports. Some varieties have produced a series of such sports, as for example Talisman (Montgomery, 1928), which produced the blood-red Mary Hart and the yellow Souvenir. The large-flowered climbing hybrid teas are all sports.

Identical results cannot be gained through repeated crossing of the same parents. The crossing of Peace with Independence produced in France the bi-coloured Grand Gala (Meilland, 1954) and in Germany the red Karl Herbst (Kordes, 1950); thus the same cross produced two entirely different roses. Nevertheless the tracing of a pedigree can give us a certain picture of the complicated processes behind the development of such varieties. We cannot as yet explain these processes with great accuracy, yet they contribute in some degree to our understanding of the complicated origins of most present-day roses.

Rose Hybridists

At the beginning of the 19th century the cultivation and hybridisation of roses was centred in France. There the hybridist worked mainly with the centifolias, damasks and gallicas. The most industrious hybridist of the day, Vibert, created many damasks as well as a series of striped varieties of *R. gallica*. Laffay also worked with the gallicas and damasks. He had already begun to cross these types with the recently imported Asian roses, and he was the originator of the hybrid perpetuals.

Around 1822 the London and Parisian commercial price-lists contained more than 350 names. In the catalogue of roses cultivated in France in 1829 more than 2,500 are listed.

At the beginning of the 19th century new varieties were still fewer than might have been expected. From 1828 to 1843, only 41 varieties were released, although there were over a dozen hybridists in France alone. The influence of the first European tea roses took effect very slowly. Then, in the years 1850-53, 79 new varieties appeared. From 1859 to 1868, 400 novelties were produced. The number of new roses grew very quickly after this: in a list compiled in 1880 there were already 5,007 species and varieties (Th. Nietner, 1880). In an account of the l'Hay rosary in France in 1902, 6,781 types and varieties and 969 wild roses are described by Gravereaux; 15,000 names are listed in the 1936 rose list (A. Jäger, 1936).

Amongst the list of hybridists in the second half of the 19th century we find: Vilmorin, Prévost, Gentilhomme, Leroy, Morreau, Roussel, Jacotot and Pradel. Half-way through this century an extensive rose nursery had been established near Lyon, and new varieties of roses were evolved there by Ducher, then Pernet-Ducher, J. B. Guillot, A. Schwartz, A. Bernaix, E. Lacharme, J. B. Croibier, J. Liebaud, Damaizin, A. Levet, Bonnaire and Gonod.

In the same period W. Paul, G. Paul, F. W. Bennett, Turner, Dickson, Broughton, Ward and Granston, among others, carried out much hybridising in the British Isles.

The cultivation of new kinds of roses became a craze, especially towards the end of the 19th century, when numerous firms offered literally dozens of novelties annually. This over-production resulted in a deterioration in the quality of roses. Growers were often out to produce novelties above all, and many new kinds were not improvements on the old, and soon disappeared.

Many countries have played their part in the creation of the extensive range of varieties available today. Because garden roses are the most popular of flowers and cultivation and propagation are relatively uncomplicated, most countries have nurseries which specialise in roses, and each year a number of new varieties are offered, all good and some outstanding. The rapid spread of new varieties almost throughout the world is facilitated by means of air transport, although customs barriers are often obstacles. In the harsher climate of the East old varieties often hold sway, especially the extra-hardy hybrid perpetuals, which nowadays are only grown to a very limited extent in the West.

PLATES

R. rubrifolia VILLARS

This rose, which is found in the mountains of Central and Southern Europe, was first cultivated in the early 19th century. The blooms are clear pink, small, with white centres and light yellow stamens, borne in bunches in midsummer and opening flat; the stems are almost thornless. Small heps, almost round and reddish brown in colour, ripen early and are carried in bunches, somewhat like dark red cherries. The foliage is most attractive and useful for flower arrangements. In a shady, cool part of the garden, the leaves are a soft grey-green with a touch of mauve; if the bush is exposed to full sunlight, they are smaller and with coppery-mauve tints. The plant grows upright to about 8 ft × 8 ft.

R. ecae AITCHISON

The name is derived from the initials — E. C. A. — of Mrs Aitchison, wife of the British Army officer who first collected these species during the Afghan War about 1880. Vivid buttercup-yellow blooms are borne on short stems during the month of May. The small, red heps are sparingly produced, and the reddish wood has many prickles. Slender and upright, this species grows to about 5 ft × 4 ft. The foliage is small, smooth and dark green. The plant prefers a sunny position and warm, well-drained soil. It is an admirable companion for the rich blue Ceanothus Delight.

26

R. *foetida bicolor* (JACQUIN) WILLMOTT

Austrian Copper. Capucine Rose.

A sport from the pure yellow *R. foetida* which is a species found in Western Asia, *R. foetida bicolor* was cultivated before 1600. The brilliant coppery-red blooms with buff reverse and prominent soft yellow stamens are unique. They are borne on dark brown stems in June, and are very freely produced on established plants. The fragrance is heavy and, to many people, somewhat unpleasant. The shrub has greyish-red prickles and parsley-green foliage which is highly susceptible to black spot.

This rose is by no means easy to grow well. It is liable to die back after a few years and is only really successful in the pure air found in country gardens. The soil must not be too rich, and a cool district is preferable, although it does very well in Cambridgeshire, which is a relatively dry county. Little or no pruning is advisable.

Careful placing in the garden is necessary, since the exceptionally vivid colour combination is hard to match in other roses, and *R. foetida bicolor* will 'quarrel' with almost any neighbour. It grows to about 9 ft × 6 ft if really happy. Virtually all the bi-coloured and multi-coloured hybrid teas can be traced back to this rose.

28

R. omeiensis pteracantha FRANCHET

This rose comes from Western China. The small, inconspicuous white blooms are produced in early summer. They have four petals instead of the five usually found in other rose species, followed by small, glossy orange-red heps, which soon fall. The rich green, finely divided leaflets give the entire bush a fern-like appearance.

The main attraction of this species lies in its remarkable prickles. These are large, wide and a translucent ruby-red when young; when mature they are both hard and sharp. Hard pruning after flowering is necessary to obtain fresh young shoots. This species grows to about 15 ft × 15 ft. It is a very popular rose for flower arrangements.

30

R. gallica L.

French Rose. Rose of Provins. Red Rose of Lancaster. Apothecary's Rose.

This species grows wild in Central and Southern Europe, in Western Asia and North America. It has been described as the foundation species from which most modern roses are derived and semi-double or double forms have probably been grown since ancient times. The Median fire-worshippers cultivated *R. gallica* in the 12th century B.C. for use in ecclesiastical ceremonies.

The Apothecary's Rose or Red Rose of Lancaster is *R. gallica officinalis*. This was at one time grown in France in the town of Provins, as well as in Mitcham, England, for the production of conserves. The semi-double, light crimson blooms of exceptional fragrance are enhanced by the prominent yellow stamens and appear about midsummer. They are followed by large, round, deep-red heps. The shrub grows upright to about 4 ft × 4 ft.

R. gallica seeds freely and germinates readily. It spreads rapidly by means of long, underground runners. V. G. Khizhanooski has described a wide range of roses belonging to this group. Tricolore de Flandre (van Houtte, 1846) which has lilac-white blooms with crimson and light red stripes is one such variety.

32

R. canina L.

A vigorous, extra-hardy shrub, often referred to as the Dog Rose. It is naturalised in both Europe and the British Isles, and occasionally in North America. The fragrant, light pink blooms are followed by ovoid, scarlet heps. A somewhat straggling grower to about 10 ft, *R. canina* was probably first used as an understock in England in 1824. Since then over 100 improved forms have been selected, mainly by English, Dutch and German nurserymen. *R. multiflora* understocks are easier to raise, but roses budded thereon may not be as long-lived.

R. centifolia major

Batavia Rose, Cabbage Rose, Provence Rose.

The blooms are pink, 3 in. in diameter and very full. They are strongly scented and usually borne singly with overlapping petals. The long, round heps are sparingly produced. This species grows to about 5 ft with an equal spread.

R. centifolia muscosa SERINGE

This species has been cultivated since before 1750. The blooms are a bright, rich pink. They are large, full, delicately scented and the flower stems are encrusted with moss-like growths. The plant flowers in summer only and grows up to 4 ft × 4 ft when established.

Souvenir de la Malmaison

Queen of Beauty and Fragrance (Béluze, 1843).

The blooms are white with a pale-pink tinge, very full and cup-like in shape. The edges of the petals are reddish, large and loosely formed. They are long-lasting, strongly scented and are freely produced, especially in autumn. The firm stems have few prickles, and the plant has an average height of about 2 ft. The majority of blooms are 'quartered, and a hot season brings out this old-timer at its best.

40

Maréchal Niel

Tea-Noisette. (Pradel, 1864)

This variety is probably a seedling from Chromatella. The blooms are a luminous golden-yellow. They are large, very full, round or cup-shaped, and are freely produced, especially in the autumn. There is a distinct tea rose scent. The leaves are a lustrous, light green. The plant has weak and pendant stems, with hooked prickles. It will sometimes flower freely out of doors, provided it is grown against a sheltered south wall and in a warm area, but it grows best nowadays in the greenhouse, where it should ultimately attain a height of up to 12 ft.

42

Zigeunerknabe

Gipsy Boy. (P. Lambert, 1909)

The blooms are a dark carmine-red shading to violet and bluish-purple. They are medium-sized, semi-double flowers, growing in clusters, which bloom once only, about mid-June. They are followed by orange-red heps. The somewhat prickly plant eventually grows to about 5 ft × 8 ft.

44

Parkfeuer

Possibly a *R. foetida* hybrid. (P. Lambert, 1906)

The colour of this rose is fiery scarlet, and there are 3 to 5 single blooms with golden-yellow stamens. These are freely produced about mid-June on thornless stems, and are very long-lasting. Growth is vigorous to about 8 ft or more.

Frühlingsduft

Joanna Hill × *R. spinosissima altaica*. (Kordes, 1949)

The blooms are pinkish-yellow shading to golden-yellow; they are large, full, well formed, strongly scented, and are freely produced in late spring. The plant grows to about 5 ft with an equal spread.

48

Carmen

R. rugosa × Princesse de Béarn. Hybrid Rugosa. (P. Lambert, 1906)

The blooms are a luminous blood-red shading to black-red; they are medium-sized, single, flat and dish-shaped with creamy-yellow stamens. They are freely produced in late June with some recurrence in certain seasons. This rose makes an effective shrub of up to 6 ft, although it is rather less bushy than some rugosa hybrids.

F. J. Grootendorst

Grootendorst, Nelkenrose. Hybrid Rugosa. (J. B. de Goey, 1918)

A cross between *R. rugosa rubra* and Mme Norbert Levavasseur, this variety is curious rather than beautiful. The blooms are bright red, fairly large and full, and borne in clusters, with dull carnation-like petals, which are fringed and jagged. They are slightly fragrant and are long-lasting. The plant flowers freely and continuously, and grows to about 7 ft × 5 ft.

52

Frau Karl Druschki

Reine des Neiges, Snow Queen, White American Beauty. (P. Lambert, 1901)

A cross between Merveille de Lyon and Mme Caroline Testout, this well-known hybrid perpetual still has its admirers. The blooms are snow-white, with only the outer edges of the petals shadowed carmine-pink on the outside. They are $4\frac{1}{2}$ in. to 6 in. in diameter, full and well formed and very long-lasting, with firm petals. The buds are long, pointed and shaded pink, borne on long, firm stems. The scentless flowers are excellent for cutting. The plant grows upright, branching to about 5 ft, with olive-green leaves. In wet weather, the majority of blooms fail to open properly, and to many people the colour is cold, suggesting a soulless perfection. Hard pruning should be avoided.

54

Mrs John Laing

Hybrid Perpetual. (H. Bennett, 1887)

The blooms are a delicate pink with lighter edges; medium to large in size, cupped and very full with 45 petals in regular formation. They are strongly scented, and the plant flowers continuously. The leaves are light green and somewhat prone to mildew, as are many of the hybrid perpetuals. This variety has very few prickles and a really tough constitution. It grows well on thin, dry soils but for best results should be planted on land in really good condition.

Ulrich Brunner Fils

Hardy American Beauty. Hybrid Perpetual. (A. Levet, 1881)

The blooms are bright cherry-red, lighter on the outside, large, fairly full, with about 30 cupped petals. They are borne singly or in twos and threes on long stems. This variety usually flowers quite freely in early autumn, and makes a big plant, attaining up to 5 ft on most soils. The fragrance is very strong.

58

Virgo

Pôle Nord × Neige Parfum. Hybrid Tea. (C. Mallerin, 1947)

The blooms are snow-white, full and medium-sized, opening flat and appearing singly or up to three in a cluster. They are scented, long-lasting and are excellent for cutting. The small, dark green leaves are susceptible to mildew.

60

Michèle Meilland

Joanna Hill × Peace. Hybrid Tea. (F. Meilland, 1945)

The blooms are whitish-pink, medium-sized, full and highly centred, with reflexing petals and some fragrance. They are very freely produced, excellent for cutting and make ideal buttonholes. The dark green foliage contrasts admirably with the delicate colouring of the shapely blooms, but is slightly susceptible to mildew. This variety is too seldom seen in present-day gardens (perhaps a reflection on the prevailing enthusiasm for size and brilliancy of colour), yet there are few roses which can be more pleasing to those who value form and refinement above all in the individual flower.

Comtesse Vandal

(Ophelia × Mrs Aaron Ward) × Souvenir de Claudius Pernet. Hybrid Tea. (M. Leenders, 1932)

The large, scented blooms are salmon-yellow on the inside and coral-red on the outside. The foliage is somewhat susceptible to mildew. Another variety which appeals to connoisseurs of form, and that does especially well in the North of England. It is happiest with the minimum of pruning.

64

Mme Caroline Testout

Mme de Tartas × Lady Mary Fitzwilliam. Hybrid Tea. (J. Pernet-Ducher, 1890)

The blooms are a light pink with brightly tinted centres and silver-pink petals on the outside. The large, full, globular flowers are usually borne singly on long, rather weak stems, and tend to come with split centres. The shrub has light green foliage and very little scent. This is one of the earlier hybrid teas, which flourishes under the most adverse conditions, including neglect.

Betty Uprichard

Hybrid Tea. (Alex Dickson, 1922)

The blooms are salmon-pink in the centre shading to carmine-red; medium-sized, shapely in the early stages but rather thin on opening, they are very freely produced, both singly and in small clusters. They have light green, glossy leaves, and long stems with few prickles which make the variety useful for cutting. This rose grows into a tall plant, up to $4\frac{1}{2}$ ft on some soils. The fragrance is reminiscent of verbena.

Geheimrat Duisberg

Golden Rapture. Hybrid Tea. (W. Kordes, 1933)

The unshaded bright yellow blooms are medium-sized, full and well formed. The colour is, however, somewhat variable, and is often rather pale. The blooms are long-lasting and excellent for cutting. This rose does well under glass and there is some fragrance.

70

Joanna Hill

Mme Butterfly × Miss Amelia Gude. Hybrid Tea. (J. H. Hill, 1928)

The blooms are light yellow, although darker in the centre; the whitish-yellow, well-formed, full flower is borne on long, firm stems; the buds are very long, and the fragrance moderate. This variety does well under glass. It is seldom grown in the British Isles, but has long been widely planted in the U.S.A. Of considerable historical importance, it has been much used by hybridists, figuring in the ancestry of Peace. It was also the pollen parent of the flame-red and yellow floribunda Shepherd's Delight (Masquerade seedling × Joanna Hill).

72

Peace

Mme A. Meilland, Gloria Dei, Gioia. Hybrid Tea. (F. Meilland, 1943)

The parentage of this remarkable rose — probably the most widely planted of all contemporary varieties — is as follows: Joanna Hill × (Chas. P. Kilham × seedling Austrian Copper) × (Chas. P. Kilham × Margaret McGredy). Peace has been widely used by hybridists.

The buds are deep yellow with pink edgings, opening to very large, full, long-lasting, somewhat globular blooms which are more or less cupped when open. The colour is again golden-yellow with pink edgings, and the overall effect varies, depending on soil and weather. In hot weather the blooms may be yellow throughout; during cool, rainy periods, the colours are intensified.

Most blooms come singly. There may be some blind (flowerless) shoots in the first crop of bloom, but if such shoots are cut back 3 or 4 inches, fresh growths which flower in the normal way will usually appear.

Peace makes an excellent standard. It is resistant to mildew and rust, but is liable to black spot in country districts. Hard pruning should be avoided and individual bushes are best spaced at least 2 ft 6 in. apart, since growth is exceptionally vigorous. The climbing sport is unreliable except in the warmer Mediterranean territories.

74

President Herbert Hoover

Sensation × Souvenir de Claudius Pernet. Hybrid Tea. (L. B. Coddington, 1929)

The blooms are copper-red with lustrous orange-red, bright pink and yellow shades; they are large, well formed, open, long-lasting, and borne on long, strong stems. The light fragrance, somewhat like the scent of horseradish, is distinctive. The sparse, leathery leaves are prone to mildew. The habit of growth is tall and lanky, so very light pruning is inadvisable. There are few better roses for cutting, especially in early autumn.

76

Crimson Glory

Cathrine Kordes seedling × W. E. Chaplin. Hybrid Tea. (W. Kordes, 1937)

The blooms are a dark velvety-red, medium to large, full, cup-shaped, long-lasting and very freely produced. If first-quality flowers are desired, considerable disbudding may be necessary. In hot weather and after heavy rain, some blooms tend to 'blue', or they may assume brownish hues. The stems also may droop a little during warm spells. The foliage persists well into late autumn and early winter. It is prone to mildew, black spot and, in areas where this is troublesome, rust. However, in many gardens Crimson Glory has been known to suffer little from fungus diseases.

For best results light to medium, rich soil and generous feeding with either farmyard manure or inorganics are advisable. Hard pruning should be avoided.

The fragrance is exceptionally strong, although both parents have relatively little scent. Crimson Glory has been much used by hybridists, and its tendency to mildew has been transmitted to some of its descendants; for example, Red Ensign (Crimson Glory × Southport) and Konrad Adenauer (Crimson Glory × Hens Verschuren). Ena Harkness (Crimson Glory × Southport) is an honourable exception.

The climbing sport can be highly recommended.

78

Crimson King

Liebesglut. Crimson Glory × Kardinal. Hybrid Tea. (W. Kordes, 1943)

The large, full blooms are blood-red, with velvet to black shading which does not fade. They are high-centred and are usually borne singly. This variety has better colour stability than Crimson Glory, and the stems are firmer, but it has not proved sufficiently free-flowering to achieve widespread popularity.

Poinsettia

Hybrid Tea. (Howard and Smith, 1938)

The blooms are a luminous scarlet, medium to large, full and borne on long, firm stems with relatively few prickles. This variety keeps its colour well and is excellent for cutting. It is widely grown under glass, but has never been really popular for bedding. Its main disadvantage is that the fragrance is slight.

82

Beautiful

Chrysler Imperial

Charlotte Armstrong × Mirandy. Hybrid Tea. (Lammerts, 1952)

The blooms are crimson, sometimes a dusky shade, full, large, somewhat rounded and strongly scented; they are borne singly on stout stems, and are long-lasting, both on the plant and when cut. They tend to 'blue' in wet weather. The dark green foliage is somewhat susceptible to mildew.

84

Contrast

Hybrid Tea. (Howard and Smith, 1937)

This is a pleasing bi-colour, which combines carmine-pink and bronze, and the reverse bronze and white. The full, shapely blooms are borne on long stems, and the leaves are large, glossy green and leathery.

86

Tzigane

Peace × J. B. Meilland. Hybrid Tea. (F. Meilland, 1951)

Another very attractive bi-colour, this rose combines vermilion and chrome-yellow. The large, full, somewhat globular blooms open rather quickly (especially in warm weather), but have better colour stability than do most bi-coloured hybrid teas. The foliage is dark green and glossy, but rather prone to mildew. This variety could flower more freely, and for best results a rich warm soil is probably necessary.

The following varieties also belong to this family of roses of two colours — red on the inside and yellow on the outside:

> Condesa de Sástago (P. Dot, 1932)
> Sultane (Meilland, 1945)
> Tanger (P. Dot, 1949)
> Hermann Teschendorff (V. Berger, 1949)
> Cleopatra (W. Kordes, 1955)
> Piccadilly (S. McGredy, 1959)
> Westminster (P. H. Robinson, 1959)

Prélude

Fantastique × [Ampère × (Charles P. Kilham × Capucine Chambard)]. Hybrid Tea.
(F. Meilland, 1954)

The blooms, bluish-violet, lilac or cobalt, are medium to large in size, and not very full,
having only 25 petals. There are few prickles, and the plant is vigorous, although not
very free-flowering, and liable to die back in winter. It is another attempt at producing
a blue rose, which still eludes the most skilful hybridists, who only succeed in producing
blue-violet, lilac and related shades; for example, Cardinal de Richelieu (Laffay, 1840),
a gallica hybrid which is a dark violet shading to blackish or slatey blue. One famous
'blue' remontant rose was Reine des Violettes (Mille-Mallet, 1860) with purple-violet and
lilac blooms, and from it came varieties like Generál Štefánik (J. Böhm, 1931).

   Other attempts at such blue or violet roses are Sterling Silver (Fisher, 1957), Lilac
Time (S. McGredy, 1956), Blue Boy (W. Kordes, 1958), Black Boy (W. Kordes, 1958),
Blue Moon (M. Tantau, 1964), Lavender Lassie (W. Kordes, 1959), Overture (Le Grice,
1960) and Intermezzo (P. Dot, 1963).

Orléans Rose

Polyantha Pompon. (Levavasseur, 1909)

This polyantha rose has semi-double blooms which are red with pink shading and whitish in the centre. The pompon edges of the petals are carmine, medium to large in size, and produced in compact upright clusters. They are long-lasting and have little scent. Through 'sporting' this variety was a parent of many well-known polyanthas including Cameo (1932), Gloria Mundi (1929) and Miss Edith Cavell (1917). All are dwarf growers.

Katharina Zeimet

White Baby Rambler. Polyantha Pompon. (P. Lambert, 1901)

The blooms are pure white, small, full and long-lasting; they are moderately fragrant, and borne in large clusters of 25 to 50 on short stems. The leaves are dark green and small.

94

Joseph Guy

Lafayette. Richmond × Rödhätte. Floribunda. (Nonin, 1924)

The blooms are luminous scarlet, shading to dark cherry-carmine. Large, semi-double, cup-shaped and long-lasting, they appear in clusters of 30 to 40 blooms, on stout stems. The low bush is hardy and grows to about 18 in. in height. It has rich, glossy green foliage.

Else Poulsen

Orléans Rose × Red Star. Floribunda. (D. T. Poulsen, 1924)

One of the earliest floribundas or hybrid polyanthas (as they were originally called), grown with the object of developing a race of free-flowering roses sufficiently hardy to withstand the rigours of Scandinavian winters. Else Poulsen bears immense quantities of clear, rose-pink, semi-double blooms on long stems. They are very long-lasting, both on the plant and when cut, but tend to 'spot' in wet weather. The dark bronze-green foliage is unfortunately markedly susceptible to mildew and black spot.

Fortschritt

Progress. Mrs Pierre S. du Pont × Gloria Mundi. Floribunda. (W. Kordes, 1933)

The large, semi-double, yellowish-pink blooms tend to lose their colour in hot weather. They are borne in small clusters and on firm stems. The light green, glossy foliage is prone to mildew.

Orange Triumph

Eva × Solarium. Floribunda. (W. Kordes, 1937)

There is rather more scarlet in the colour than the name implies. The small, full, cupped blooms are borne in large clusters and are indifferent both to continuous rain and hot sun. The glossy green foliage is slightly susceptible to mildew.

Pinocchio

Rosenmärchen. Eva×Golden Rapture. Floribunda. (W. Kordes, 1940)

The blooms are salmon-pink with yellowish shading. Small, full and rosette-shaped, they are borne in large clusters and are very long-lasting, both on the plant and when cut. This most beautiful variety has two faults which have always restricted its popularity: the petals are soft and therefore easily damaged by rain, and some blooms exhibit reddish spots which tend to mar the overall colour. The bright green, leathery foliage is resistant to both black spot and mildew. Pinocchio makes a most attractive standard, since it is seldom out of flower.

Alain

(Guinée × Wilhelm) × Orange Triumph. Floribunda. (F. Meilland, 1946)

The full blooms are blood-red and come in large clusters. The dark green, glossy foliage is fairly resistant to fungus diseases. This variety has never received the recognition it surely merits, since it has few faults, although it lacks the extreme vigour of some later reds. In small gardens this is, however, a definite advantage.

106

Fashion

Pinocchio × Crimson Glory. Floribunda. (E. S. Boerner, 1947)

A most beautiful colour which is by no means easy to describe: coral-peach, salmon-peach, orange-salmon and coral-salmon are attempts to define its hue.

The full blooms are medium to large in size; they keep their colour in hot weather, although the open flower is not particularly shapely, and sometimes drops its petals too quickly. Fashion is delightful for cutting, provided one cuts when the buds are well advanced. It has a distinct, wild-rose fragrance.

Unfortunately the ample, glossy green foliage is susceptible to fungus diseases, especially rust and black spot. Fashion does not winter well in some areas, although in built-up areas, where rust and black spot are of little if any significance, Fashion will often do very well. Elsewhere, Decapo (M. Leenders, 1960) should be tried. This variety is somewhat similar in colour and is decidedly less prone to disease.

Masquerade

Goldilocks × Holiday. Floribunda. (E. S. Boerner, 1949)

This variety introduced a completely new colour 'scheme' which still remains immensely popular. The buds are deep yellow with red splashes, opening to yellow which passes to salmon-flame, and finally deep red, all these colours being present at the same time on each cluster. The semi-double blooms are small, but are very freely produced in large clusters of 8 to 25 flowers, which are agreeably fragrant. The plentiful, dark green, glossy foliage shows some resistance to fungus diseases.

Masquerade is unaffected by continuous rain. The blooms are useful for cutting. If the buds are cut and allowed to open in water, the open blooms are more yellow than those opening on the plant. Masquerade is excellent as a standard and is sometimes grown as a hedge. Its only fault is that there are rather long gaps between each flush of bloom.

The climbing sport is very satisfactory.

Red Favourite

Holländerin, Schweizer Gruss. Karl Weinhausen × Cinnabar. Floribunda. (M. Tantau, 1951)

The blooms are blood-red and velvety; semi-double and large in size, they are unaffected by weather extremes. The dark green, glossy foliage is resistant to black spot. This variety is somewhat shorter in growth than many present-day floribundas, being unlikely to exceed 2 ft in height. Growth is, however, sturdy and there are few better varieties for standards. Lilli Marlene (W. Kordes, 1959) is often termed an improvement on Red Favourite, but although it blooms more freely, the colour, a bright crimson, lacks the appeal of the older rose.

Gruss an Aachen

Frau Karl Druschki × Franz Deegen. Floribunda. (P. Geduldig, 1909)

The blooms are whitish-pink or yellowish-pink, with salmon-orange centres and some reddish shading; they are very large, very full, and flat like a camellia or paeony. The old blooms finally pass to creamy-white. They are pleasantly fragrant, and are enhanced by the rich green, leathery foliage. The plant is of dwarf habit, growing to about 2 ft in height.

Independence

Kordes Sondermeldung, Reina Elisenda. Crimson Glory × Baby Château. Floribunda. (W. Kordes, 1951)

Another variety whose colour is hard to describe. Orange-red, brick-red, geranium-red, cinnabar, red lead, are among the epithets used by various writers, and one authority describes it as pure scarlet with blackish outer petals. The medium-sized, well-formed, full blooms open slowly and are very long-lasting, both on the plant and in the house.

Independence dislikes the rain and is only at its best in really sunny weather. When disbudded, it will give blooms of hybrid tea quality.

116

1972

Rimosa

Goldilocks × Perla de Montserrat. Floribunda. (F. Meilland, 1959)

The blooms are pure yellow, shading to cream. They are of medium size, semi-double and open flat. This variety is of dwarf habit up to 2 ft in height, and is accordingly ideal for the front of a rose bed or border. Other recent varieties suitable for the same purpose include Ambrosia (A. Dickson, 1962), Golden Slippers (von Abrams, 1961), Ascot (A. Dickson, 1962), Hit Parade (A. Dickson, 1962), Paddy McGredy (S. McGredy, 1962), Red Favourite (M. Tantau, 1951) and Marlena (R. Kordes, 1964).

Eva

Robin Hood × J. C. Thornton. Shrub Rose. (W. Kordes, 1933)

The blooms are carmine-red, with white centres; they are semi-double, and borne in immense clusters. The plant is very vigorous, to about 6 ft.

120

Berlin

Eva × Peace. Shrub Rose. (W. Kordes, 1949)

The blooms are fiery vermilion, single with yellow stamens, fragrant and very long-lasting. This rose flowers unusually freely from the beginning of summer until the frosts begin. The dark green, leathery foliage is resistant to fungus diseases. A tough, extra-hardy variety, this plant is best treated as a specimen bush with very little pruning. It will then attain 5 ft with a spread of 3 ft.

122

Dorothy Perkins

R. wichuraiana × Mme Gabriel Luizet. Rambler. (Jackson and Perkins, 1901)

The blooms are a delicate salmon-pink, but a darker pink when in full bloom. They are small and fully double, borne in large clusters and long-lasting. The dark green foliage is highly susceptible to mildew. The long, flexible growths are relatively easy to train; they droop naturally and a weeping standard can therefore be made with little difficulty. Dorothy Perkins is equally suitable for pillar, arch, pergola, hedge or screen, but not for walls where it readily succumbs to mildew, as do most of the older wichuraiana ramblers.

124

Veilchenblau

Violet Blue. Rambler. (J. C. Schmidt, 1909)

The blooms are pinkish-violet and amethyst-violet, shaded with a white centre, but steel-blue when in full bloom. They are semi-double and cupped, flowering in clusters of 5 to 30 blooms, with a pleasing fragrance. This rose blooms once during midsummer. The light green foliage is somewhat susceptible to mildew. A very vigorous variety, the plant grows to about 20 ft when well established, and will thrive on a north wall.

American Pillar

(*R. wichuraiana* × *R. setigera*) × a red Hybrid Perpetual. Rambler. (van Fleet, 1902)

The blooms are carmine-red, with white centres and numerous yellow stamens; they are borne in very large clusters. The extra-vigorous growths are difficult to manage on the normal 8 to 10 ft pillar, and this variety is best grown on an arch or pergola, so that it has plenty of room to throw out its long basal shoots.

128

Paul's Scarlet Climber

Paul's Carmine Pillar × Soleil d'Or. Climber. (W. Paul, 1915)

The blooms are a luminous scarlet-crimson; medium-sized, semi-double and cup-shaped, they are long-lasting and there are occasional later flowers. This rose stands up well to heavy rain, but dislikes very hot weather. It is slightly susceptible to black spot and mildew. The plant tends to become bare towards the base after a few years, and it may be advisable to cut back one or more older shoots to within 12 in. of soil level. It is suitable for pillar, wall or fence.

New Dawn

Sport from Dr. W. van Fleet. Climber. (Dreer, 1930)

The blooms are light pink, large, full and long-lasting; they are produced freely and continuously from June to autumn. There is a distinct, wild-rose fragrance. The dark green foliage is resistant to disease; this variety is ideal for pillars.

132

Cocktail

Climber. (F. Meilland, 1957)

The blooms are fiery-scarlet with vividly yellow centres when in full bloom, the difference later disappearing. They are single, opening in clusters. A modern variety, this rose is a moderate grower of semi-climbing habit, best grown as a free-blooming shrub.

134